Letters to Edward

by Wendy Body

GW00360819

Contents

Longman

Edinburgh Gate
Harlow, Essex

7, Queen Ann Road
Upton-on-Sea
21st August

Dear Edward,

It is raining and I am fed up. Mum said, "Why don't you write to Edward?" So I am. Auntie Mandy gave me this paper to write on. Do you like it? I haven't seen you for a long time so I'm going to tell you what I've been doing.

We have been at Auntie Mandy's house for a week. I've been on the beach lots of times. I made three sandcastles. The best one was really big and Auntie Mandy got me a flag to stick in the top. But a horrible boy came along and he kicked my sandcastle to bits and then he ran away. I cried and Auntie Mandy ran after the boy. She told his mum and dad what he had done. They made him come back and say sorry to me. Then he had to make me a new sandcastle. It was OK but it wasn't as good as the one I made. I kicked it all down. Mum was cross but Auntie Mandy laughed and so did the boy's dad.

I am getting good at swimming. I can swim a bit without my armbands now. When I am as big as you I shall be able to swim a long way. I like swimming in the sea but Mum won't let me go in by myself. One day I was in the sea with Auntie Mandy and some seaweed got caught on my legs. I thought it was a sea monster come to get me. Auntie Mandy said, "We don't have sea monsters in Upton-on-Sea, only sand monsters." And then we made a monster on the sand. Mum took a photo of it but it was no good because she forgot to put a film in the camera. So I'll draw you a picture instead.

3

This is what it looked like:

We went shopping yesterday. I got a new T-shirt with a big ~~round~~ rainbow on it. You could have your name put on it too. So I did. I got a present to take home for Nana as well. It's a dog made out of shells. Do you know why I got a dog? It's because Nana and Gramps' dog has just had puppies. Nana phoned Mum to tell us. There are six puppies. Three are black, two are brown and black and one is black with a brown patch on its head. I wish I could have one. I'd have the one with the brown patch and call it Patchy.

I asked Mum if I could have it but she said no. She said it might eat Hammy and then what would I do? I don't think it would eat Hammy. I think Mum doesn't want a puppy and she was just saying that. I bet if I asked Nana she would let me have Patchy. What do you think? Shall I ask her?

Mum has just come in and said that it has stopped raining and we can go out. So I'm going to stop writing to you. Anyway, my hand hurts because I've done so much writing. Will you write a letter to me and tell me what you've been doing? Will you tell me what you think I should do about Patchy?

Lots of love
from,

Lindie

P.S. This is a picture
of me in my
new T-shirt.

Friday 4th May

My Dear Eddie,

It was so lovely to get a letter from you this morning – it made a rainy day turn into a sunny one.

I'm so glad that you liked your birthday present. I'm glad that it fitted you! I did think that it might be a bit big for you so it's good to know that it fits you so well. Grandad said that next time we see you he will get you some new boots to go with it.

Yes, I am much better now, thank you, dear. I feel like my old self again. I haven't had 'flu for years and I had forgotten how bad it makes you feel. It was a good job that Grandad didn't catch it as well.

Yes, Eddie, of course you can come and stay with us for a week in the holidays. You know

6

that we always love having you to stay with us. Grandad is always talking about what we can do next time you come to stay. I think he wants to take you ten-pin bowling again. This time, perhaps you will let him win! Let us know if there is anything else that you would like to do.

We had a day out in Bristol last week. I wanted to take some photographs with the new camera I had for my birthday. They came out very well, I think. I took a lot of the bridge at Clifton so I'm sending one to you. Do you remember when we went there and saw the hot air balloons last August? I do love seeing hot air balloons up in the sky! When I went to the shops on Monday, I saw this postcard of hot air ballons. I got it for you because I thought you might like to put it on the wall in your bedroom.

We have been spending a lot of time in the garden this week. Grandad has finished making the new pond and it looks lovely. We have seen two frogs in there already! Next week we are going to get some fish to put in it. I think we will get about ten small goldfish - nothing too much or too fancy. I think we will have to put a net over the water. We need a net to stop Mrs Brown's cat fishing for its tea!

By the way ... some new people have just moved into the house down the road. They have come from Hong Kong and they have three children - two little girls and a boy who is about your age. I hope you like him and that you can make friends with him. It would be nice for you to have someone of your own age to play with when you come to stay with us, wouldn't it?

Clifton

I rang your Uncle Nick last night. He said that baby Tom is doing really well and that he has grown quite a bit. Grandad and I are going to see them next week. It will be lovely to see the baby again. It will be lovely to see you too, dear, when you come to stay.

Till then,

All our love to you – and to your mum and dad,

Grandma and Grandad

x x x x x x

Dear Ed,

Gran has let me put in a note of my own! I'm really looking forward to seeing you in the holidays. Did Gran tell you that I am looking forward to going ten-pin bowling again? This time, my lad, I'm going to win!! I thought that we could go fishing as well. My friend Jack has a cottage by the river and the fishing is good there. By the way, we put the fish back in the water - we don't keep them. I can see it now ... you'll catch a big one and I'll get a little one (or I won't get one at all!)

Talking about fishing, the new pond is looking really good. I'm looking forward to getting some fish for it next week. I'm thinking of getting about twenty or thirty big goldfish – you know, the ones with long fancy tails. It will cost a bit but Gran won't mind.

Gran wants to get this in the post so I must stop. Glad you liked the new football kit!

Love from
Grandad

The Madhouse!
(You know where!)
Saturday

Hi Ed!

Thanks ever so much for the card you sent us – and for your letter too. It was really good to hear from you. Tom is now two weeks old. He sleeps and has a feed and sleeps and has a feed ... that's about all really! Oh yes and sometimes he cries ... oh boy, can that baby cry!! He usually cries when I'm trying to work. (I've just started the illustrations for another book about that crazy pig and his friend the chicken.)

He (Tom, that is – not the crazy chicken!) has blue eyes, no teeth and a little bit of fluffy hair. He has tiny little hands but he can hold your finger very tightly. (He can hang on so well that he might grow up to be like Tarzan and swing through the trees!! Watch out, Ed, in a few year's time you might hear someone going aaaaoooaaaaoooaaah! and it will be Tom swinging on your front door!!)

Some people think he looks like me (poor baby!) and some people think he looks like his mum. This is what I think he looks like:

Tom is great and I love him to bits (even if he does keep us awake at nights!)

I really enjoyed reading your letter. The bit about your dad getting stuck at the top of the ladder made me laugh. When we were kids, he climbed up a tree to fetch my ball. He got stuck up there, too! I had to go and fetch your grandad to help him down. We both got told off – me because I kicked the ball up into the tree and broke some branches and your dad because he got stuck and broke some more branches.

Great news about the football match! I was really pleased to hear that your team won. We had a good game last week. We won – even though I did let in two goals. You should have seen the chap who scored them – he was at least eight feet tall and four feet wide. (His legs were like tree trunks – good for Tom to swing on in a few year's time!!!)

Talking of Tom, I can hear that "I'm-wet-come-and-change-me!" cry so I'd better go and see to him. Give our love to your mum and dad and I hope you'll be able to come and see us soon.

Much love,
Yours,

Uncle Nick

Upmoore Primary School

Moorend Lane, Upworth
UP7 5LM
Tel: 32758 623951

14th June

Dear Edward,

Since you were good enough to write me a letter of apology, I think it is only fair of me to reply by letter as well. I was very disappointed in your behaviour. I really like having you in my school, Edward, but I don't like the way you behaved towards Ben.

I am pleased to hear that you are sorry for what you have done. There are two things I hope you will learn from what has happened. The first thing is that you must do your best to control your temper. I know that you don't fly into a rage very often, Edward, but every time that you do there is always the danger that you will hurt someone – just as you hurt Ben.

All of us get angry sometimes, but the important thing is to try not to hurt other people. You can hurt someone with words just as much as you can hurt people by hitting or kicking them. Sometimes the words can hurt more because they stay with us in our memories. I am four times older than you, Edward, but I can still remember something hurtful that my brother said to me when he was in a temper when I was about your age. I know he didn't mean it ... but the point is that it was so hurtful that I still remember it.

16

17

The second thing I want you to learn is that we should try to understand and respect everyone — everyone, Edward, and not just our friends.

You have a lot of friends and you are good at sport but not everyone is the same as you. Some people find it hard to make friends and they may not like doing the same things as you do. Some boys are not good at sport but this does not mean that they are not good at anything! Everyone is good at something and just because someone is different from you, it does not mean that you should treat them differently.

There is something I want you to do for me, Edward. I would like you to think about Ben and see if you can write down all the things he is good at. It will help you to show him that you really didn't mean what you said when you write to him. Yes, Edward, I know you have already said you are sorry to him but I want you to write a letter of apology to him as well.

When you have written your letter, that will be the end of the matter. You, I hope, will have learned something from what has happened and I will carry on thinking of you as the kind and helpful boy that I know you really are.

Yours sincerely,

Mr A. E. Stone

Headteacher

October 28th

Dear Edward,

Thank you very much for your letter – I did enjoy reading it. I really like the sound of the story you have just written.

Now let me try to answer some of your questions ...

My first book, which was a story called Clay Horses, was published a very long time ago – before you were born, in fact! Since then I have had a lot more books published. Most of them are stories for younger children, but some (like Estelle's Reward) are for children of about your age.

Where do I get my ideas from? Well, ideas can come from all sorts of things and in all sorts of ways. One of my books is called The Bracelet and this is how I got the idea for that one. I always wear a bracelet and when I'm thinking I often play around with it. One day I was wearing a bracelet which has four or five brown stones called tiger's eyes set into it. I suddenly thought, 'I wonder what would happen if this was a magic bracelet and if you pressed the stones you became invisible?' That was it – I had the idea for a story! I find ideas for stories often come when you look at something and ask "What if ...?" questions about it.

It's very hard to say how long a story takes me. I do write quickly but some things take much longer to write than others. What really takes the time is how long you spend making changes. Sometimes I spend a really long time revising and can write several drafts. When I'm happy with it I send it off to my publisher. Sometimes she says it's fine and sometimes she asks me to make a few changes – so I spend even more time on it.

When I'm at home I use my computer for all my writing. But I spend quite a lot of time travelling on trains so I often do some writing then. I have a notebook which I always keep in my bag and I write in pencil. Sometimes the writing gets very wiggly because the train is going so fast. When I'm putting it into my computer I often have a hard job reading what I've written!

Yes, Edward, I do like animals. We have two small dogs called Muffin and Merlin. They are Yorkshire terriers and they are brothers. Their favourite toy is a squeaking carrot. They spend a lot of time making it squeak and then one will push it under an armchair and bark until the other one pulls it out again. Mad!

Pelican Big Books

Estelle's Reward
by **Wendy Body**

Illustrated by Jenny Press

Pelican Big Books

Anna's Amazing Multi-Coloured Gla
by **Wendy Body**

Illustrated by **Piers Harper**

In the toyshop
by **Wendy Body**

Illustrated by Adrienne Geoghegan

I'm not sure what I would want to do if I wasn't a writer. I think I'd like to be a famous singer or a painter – I'm not sure which. What do you want to be when you grow up, Edward? You said you like writing and football so perhaps you will be a writer or a footballer?

I think there are two good things about being a writer. One is seeing your book when it is first published – which will be months after you've finished writing it. The second is being able to create pictures for other people to enjoy. But they are pictures made with words. I have to make pictures with words because I can't draw! I wish I could, because then I might be able to illustrate some of my own books. Mind you, I love seeing the characters I have created brought to life by someone else! One of the nicest things I have is the original water colour painting of one page from one of my books. It hangs in my hall so that the sun can't fade the colours.

Well, Edward, I think I've answered most of your questions so I'll stop now. Thank you again for writing to me,

With very best wishes,

Yours sincerely,

Wendy Body

Wendy Body

Supercrunch Crisps Ltd

Weatherfield Way, Bolchester BL41 14U

15 September

Dear Edward,

I am writing to reply to your letter of 11 September. I am so very sorry that you had such a shock when you were eating a packet of our crisps.

I can imagine what it must have been like. There you were with your mouth open to crunch a Supercrunch Crisp and what did you see? Not just a crisp but half a beetle as well!

It was very helpful of you to send the crisp as evidence. You packed it so carefully in cotton wool and a matchbox that we were able to see for ourselves this horrible sight.

We are so sorry. Here at Supercrunch Crisps we pride ourselves on our high standards. The only extra thing that goes into our crisps is our hope that our customers will enjoy them. We certainly don't like the idea of adding beetles for extra value. (I'm sure you were joking when you said this?)

22

I really can't explain how the beetle got into your crisps. Our factory is very clean and hygienic and we have never had anything like this happen before.

However, we would like to try to make up for your unfortunate experience by sending you a gift with our compliments. I have arranged for a box of Supercrunch Crisps to be sent to you. The box contains forty packets in assorted flavours so that should keep you and your friends going for a while.

Please accept my apologies once more,

Yours sincerely,

M Bloomfield

Ms M. Bloomfield

Customer Services Manager

Supercrunch Crisps Ltd
Weatherfield Way, Bolchester BL41 14U

20 September

Dear Edward Berkley,

Re your complaint about our product. If, as you say, you found a small creature in a packet of our Supercrunch Crisps, then I am sorry. However, I do find it difficult to understand how such a thing could have come to pass. Our factory is very clean and hygienic and we have never had anything like this happen before.

Are you quite certain that the beetle was actually in the bag of Supercrunch Crisps? I am not suggesting that this is some schoolboy joke made in the hope of getting free crisps out of us; perhaps you were simply mistaken and the creature crawled into the bag when you were not looking.

Whatever the truth of the matter, I trust that you and your friends will continue to buy and enjoy what are undoubtedly the best crisps in the world.

Yours faithfully,

C. J. Green
Managing Director

Westway Primary School
Lodge Road,
Greenhill,
GR2 9LR

2nd October

Dear Edward,

Did your teacher warn your class that you would be getting letters from our school? Our teacher put the names of everyone in your class in a box for us to pick one out. We took it in turns to choose one and I got yours. So ... do you want to be my penfriend? I hope so. Anyway, I suppose I'd better tell you about myself.

I am nine years old and my name is Becky. I have got long dark hair and a cat and a dog. My cat is white and she's called Snowball. My dog is brown with a

26

patch of black fur over one eye. Guess what his name is? No, it's not PATCH, it's Winky. I've got a sister, too, but she is only five and a real pain sometimes.

Do you like football? I do. I play for a team called Westway Juniors but when I'm ten I reckon I'll make it into the school team. My favourite football team is Man U and I've got a Man U kit and a Man U picture above my bed. What's your favourite team?

Here's a list of questions I would like you to answer. When you write back, you can tell me what you want to know about me. (You WILL write back, won't you?!)

1. What do you look like?
2. What is your star sign? (I'm Taurus.)

3. Have you got any brothers or sisters?

4. Which pop group do you like best?

5. Who is your favourite author and what is your favourite book?

6. Do you like Star Wars films? (I do.)

7. Do you like swimming? (I do.)

8. What is it like being in your school?

9. Who is your best friend?

10. Have you got any pets?

My teacher's name is Mr Bishop and I like being in his class. Although he's good fun and tells jokes, he makes us work hard too. Sometimes he gets cross because I talk too much but I know he likes me all the same.

Our headteacher is called Mr Singh. He's nice, he's got this really smiley face and bushy eyebrows.

What do you like best in school? Apart from Games, I like doing English. We have something called Literacy Hour every day. Mr Bishop says the whole world is doing it, but I guess he's joking. What happens in your Literacy Hour if you have one? Wouldn't it be funny if we were doing the same books?

I quite like Art, too. I can draw horses pretty well now. This is my sure-fire method. I start with the head shape then I do the ears. Next I do the neck with the mane and then I do the body. Finally I do the legs and the tail.

Here you are ... a Becky Winston Special just for you!

I didn't get this letter done in school so I'm finishing it off at home now. It's almost teatime and we are having pizza. I love pizza, don't you? Winky likes it, too (well, the crusty bits on the outside, not the soggy bit in the middle) but I get told off if I give him any because mum says he's getting overweight. I've just been reading a

story to my sister (mainly for a bit of peace and quiet). It's her favourite (she must have heard it a million times!) It's called OWL BABIES and it's actually a good book for little kids. Now she's watching telly and I'm writing this.

No, I'm not. I've got to stop because Dad is shouting that the pizza is ready.

Write to me soon,

Your new penfriend,

Becky Winston